BOOK EIGHT

Falling Upwards

SIMON & SCHUSTER
YOUNG BOOKS
IN ASSOCIATION WITH CHANNEL FOUR TELEVISION.

Available from all good bookshops.

For further information on the series, write to:
The Marketing Department,
Simon & Schuster Young Books,
Campus 400, Maylands Avenue,
Hemel Hempstead,
Herts HP2 7EZ

Duo Uno Trio   Brenda   Ginger   Davenport

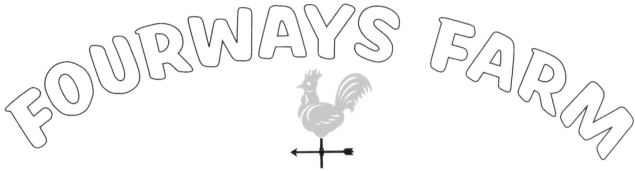

FOURWAYS FARM

Falling Upwards

Dudley   Martha   Godfrey

Text adapted from the scripts of Chris Ellis
based on an original idea by Tom Stanier.

Science Adviser: Malcolm Ward
Science Notes: Sally Nankivell-Aston
Design: Between the Lines
Illustrations: Steve Smallman based on
puppets by Alan Platt and
sets by Max Stewart.

The television programmes on which this work
is based were produced for Channel Four Television
and Nederlandse Onderwijs Televisie
by Case Television Limited.

First published in Great Britain in 1994 by
Simon & Schuster Young Books, Campus 400, Maylands
Avenue, Hemel Hempstead, Herts HP2 7EZ.

British Library Cataloguing in Publications Data available.
ISBN: 0 7500 1643 4

I can see a thing or two from my high perch up above Fourways Farm. There's always something interesting going on down there. Right now the rats are up to their naughty tricks, and the other animals have no idea what's going to hit them!

"Mmm, this is nice and peaceful," sighed Martha.

"Too peaceful," grumbled Godfrey.
"There's bound to be a catch."

"Oh, Godfrey! What could possibly go
wrong?" asked Martha.

Just as Martha dozed off, Uno dropped a pebble right on to her head.

"Ouch!" cried Martha. "Who did that?"

"Hee, hee, hee!" giggled the rats, and dropped an acorn on to Davenport's head.

"I say, someone has tapped me on the head now!" he grumbled.

9

"Huh!" moaned Godfrey. "Nothing ever happens to me."
Suddenly an apple landed on his head.
"At least, only painful things," he added, glumly.

The rats were laughing so much that Uno lost his balance
and came tumbling down the tree.

"I might have known it was you lot," said Davenport.

"Ah, but it made you think, didn't it?" asked Uno. "For instance, do things always fall down?"

"Of course they do!" snapped Davenport.

"Wrong!" said Uno. Trio can fall upwards."

The animals wanted proof, so Uno led them into the barn to demonstrate how Trio could fall upwards.

"Ready?" he called.
"Yes!" answered Trio, nervously.

"Fall upwards!" commanded Uno.

Trio rose high into the air and then came down again.

"Very interesting," purred Ginger, creeping out of a dark corner. "I don't suppose you could do that little trick again, Uno?"

"Right then," gulped Uno. "Trio – fall upwards!" he shouted.

Nothing happened.

"Fall upwards!" he yelled, this time at the top of his voice.

Trio started to go up and up, pulled by a secret wire - but suddenly she stopped and was left hanging in the air.

Ginger had discovered who was pulling the other end of the wire. It was Duo, hiding behind the straw bales!

"Duo! Duo!" cried poor Trio. "Get me down!"
But Ginger had started to tickle Duo.
"No! Stop it! Hee, hee!" Duo giggled, and let go of the wire.

Trio came whizzing down and landed
slap-bang on top of Uno!

That night the animals had a lot to think about.

"Balloons don't fall down," said Davenport. "They float down."

"And birds don't fall down either," added Martha. "They flap their wings and push downwards."

"But there's nothing to push downwards on," puzzled Godfrey.

"Maybe there is . . . " said Martha.

NOTES FOR PARENTS AND TEACHERS

This book is about how the rats try to fool the other animals into thinking that Trio can fall upwards rather than downwards. The story can be used to develop your child's ideas about gravity and the way that different objects fall to the ground when dropped.

1 Dropping objects

Collect together objects that travel to the ground at different speeds and in different ways including: feathers, balls, a paper plate, a small toy figure, two pieces of paper (one screwed up into a ball), a sycamore seed and two balloons (one blown up). Hold each object in turn at about shoulder level and ask your child to predict what the object will do when you let go of it. Drop each object and ask your child to describe what actually happens.

2 Making a parachute

Then ask your child to suggest a way of making the toy figure's journey to the ground slower, and therefore safer. Use the paper plate and four pieces of cotton thread to make a parachute and attach the toy figure to it. Drop the parachute and see what happens.

PS:

You can extend activity 2 by using different materials to make parachutes and finding out which type of material makes the best one.